G000122769

The Spotted Unicorn

The Diaries of Chi Wen Tzu

Edited by Roger McGough

VIKING

VIKING

Published by the Penguin Group
Penguin Books Ltd, 27 Wrights Lane, London W8 5TZ, England
Penguin Putnam Inc., 375 Hudson Street, New York 10014, USA
Penguin Books Australia Ltd, Ringwood, Victoria, Australia
Penguin Books, Canada Ltd, 10 Alcorn Avenue, Toronto, Ontario, Canada MV4 3B2
Penguin Books (NZ) Ltd, 182–190 Wairau Road, Auckland 10, New Zealand

Penguin Books Ltd, Registered Offices: Harmondsworth, Middlesex, England

First published 1998
1 3 5 7 9 10 8 6 4 2

Copyright © Roger McGough, 1998
Illustrations copyright © Satoshi Kitamura, 1998
The moral right of the author has been asserted

Set in 11 on 15 pt Monotype Ellington
Designed in QuarkXpress on an Apple Macintosh
Printed in Great Britain by The Bath Press

A CIP catalogue record for this book is available from the British Library

ISBN 0–670–87974–6

'A philosopher dies – the unicorn is spotted.'

– Ancient Chinese

季文子三思而後行　子聞之曰　再思斯可矣

(CHI WEN TZU)

THRICE
THINK
THEN
AFTER-
WARDS
DO

CONFUCIUS
HEAR
THIS
SAID

TWICE
THINK
IS
FINE

Preface

'Chi Wen Tzu always thought three times before taking action. Twice would have been quite enough.'

Having been an admirer of the great Chinese philosopher Confucius for many years, I was reading through Book 5 of the *Analects* (the choicest pearls of his wisdom) when I was suddenly struck by the above. Who was this Chi Wen Tzu? And what manner of man always reflected thrice before acting? My research led me to the discovery of a number of diaries written by an indecisive and yet inventive and brilliant poet, whose journal will shed surprising new light on a little-known period of ancient history.

R McG
London, 1998

Tonight, young wife lying naked
on panda-skin rug. Full moon
hanging in sky like Chinese lampshade
(one of those round white ones).

At sight of fragrant body
its hills and valleys
bathed in silver light
am overcome with desire.

Wonder what course of action to take?

> *Make love, then and there?*

> *Make tea, then make love?*

> *Open bottle of rice-wine,*
> *write up day's events in diary,*
> *relax in warm bath,*
> *then make love?*

Wife gone home to mother for fortnight.
Not like being woken up at 4 a.m.
by drunken diarist.

Tonight, house cold and empty
as purse of K'ung Fu Tzu.

Have not eaten all day
so think about what to do for supper:

> *Send out for take-away?*

> *Drop in at Hard Wok Café?*

> *Crack open third bottle of rice-wine
> and see how feel later?*

[*Editor's Note:* No diary entries for several weeks.]

K'ung Fu Tzu (or, Confucius
as now call himself) pop in
on way to Aphorism Conference.

Over dish of lapsang souchong
he relate long boring parable
about indecision and procrastination.

Fifteen minutes later
he repeat same parable.
Fifteen minutes later
heart sink as illustrious duffer
embark once more on inane ramble.

Consider three courses of action:

> *Feign bout of sleeping sickness?*

> *Allow to finish. He is, after all, old man;
> then laugh softly like moth alighting
> on moonlit breast of young wife?*

> *Interrupt?*

Interrupting, I say:
'Twice would have been quite enough.'

Innocent remark have strange effect
on esteemed Master
who jot it down on back of hand, rise up and go.

Nothing doing at home
so journey to mountains
to find cave in which to meditate.

All caves full.

China big country
and although many wise men
only so many caves.

Decide on course of action:

Transcend to higher astral plane?

Descend to hire private plane?

*Give idea elbow and give young wife
nice surprise on panda skin?*

Returning home along river-bank
pause to make water
against trunk of weeping willow.
Suddenly, on rickety bridge
see young wife in arms of Lin Fang!
Heart stop, turning off water.
End of rainbow spatter over feet
disturbing nesting ducks, who take flight.

Consider carefully what to do:

Kill wife?

Kill Lin Fang?

Design dinner service?

Confucius call at humble home
on way to bamboo shoot.
Very apologetic about misbehaviour
of Lin Fang, favoured disciple.

Young wife enter, looking sheepish
(on all fours, going 'Baa, baa').
Everybody laugh, and Confucius
beg me forgive and forget.

Chi Wen Tzu reflect on three choices:

>   *Forgive and forget?*

>   *Forgive now, kill later?*

>   *Have wife for supper with mint sauce?*

T'ai Chi exercises interrupted
by owner of porcelain factory
who is much taken with design
for plates. Except for flying ducks.

He ask, why three different sizes?
I explain there is a daddy duck,
mummy duck and baby duck.
He nod, but go away unconvinced.

Wonder what to put in place of ducks:

Flock of budgies?

Swarm of locusts?

Pair of bluebirds?

Waking with sublime images in mind
arise and sit beneath mulberry tree
to compose poem for young wife.
It is entitled 'Poem for Ning'.

'Your eyelashes are like the finest willow-twigs
Your cheeks are whiter than the lily
Your teeth brighter than the scales
        of the Sacred Dragon
Your brow smoother than polished jade
Your body welcoming and transparent
        as a mountain stream.'

Deservedly pleased with poem, wonder whether to:

Show to young wife immediately?

*Put away until 2nd August and save
money on birthday present?*

*Change title and slip to exceedingly
symmetrical daughter of factory-owner?*

Young wife try to appease husband
with gift of poetry book. Title?
New Generation Chinese Poetry.

Finding poems too long and impenetrable
decide to invent short, snappy verse-form.

With aid of abacus
Chi Wen Tzu ponder on its construction.

   *First, how many lines
then how many syllables.
   Eureka! Haiku.*

[*Editor's Note:* Having invented the haiku (and sold the copyright to a consortium of Japanese poets), Chi Wen Tzu wrote several thousand before going on to invent the sonnet, the villanelle, the limerick and the Malaysian pantoum.

The few that have survived illustrate the wide breadth of his poetic vision, and seem almost to pre-date some of the best-loved poems in English literature.]

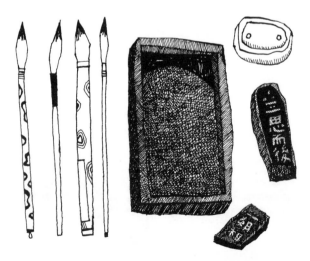

There is some corner
of a foreign paddy-field
Forever China.

Wandering lonely
as cloud. Then heart leaps. Behold –
Golden pagodas!

On snowy evening
stopping by neighbour's dark woods
horse leaves steaming gift.

Sing of dappled things!
Freckled legs and pickled eggs
Budgies' wings. Nipples.

In forest of night
Panda! Panda! burning bright
Soon, bedroom carpet.

This is the night-mail
crossing the border. Oh no
Leaves on track – turn back.

If you can keep head
in time of Revolution
– you will be a man (darin).

Mongol hordes swoop down
on missionary and wife.
Noble six hundred!

O my luve's like red
red rose, pink, pink carnation
green, green grass of home.

Do not go gentle
Rage Rage Rage Rage Rage Rage Rage
Against lots of things.

Far out in cold sea
And not waving but drowning
Man see funny side.

They mess you about
Most honourable parents
(But who gives a fuck?)

Young wife growing bored of late
which cause much concern
as memory of Lin Fang weigh heavily on loin.

Too much time on delicate but idle hand.

Confucius he say: 'Woman without hobby
like monkey brains without black-bean sauce.'

So husband choose suitable pastime:

> *Buy her noodle-work kit?*

> *Acupuncture-repair outfit?*

> *Piano?*

Hearing chopsticks on piano
enter music-room to find
young wife at keyboard
eating chow mein. Very angry.

Chew over possibilities:

Chastise young wife?

*Part-exchange greasy piano
for new young wife?*

Invent xylophone?

Form company to market
new line in tableware:
'Blue Willow Pattern, China'.

Chi Wen Tzu soon rich man.
Already orders flooding in
from all over country (like guests).

To celebrate good fortune, throw party.
Already guests flooding in
from all over country (like orders).

Tonight will be night to remember
but am nervous, so consider three choices.
Shall I:

> *Assume lotus position and breathe deeply?*

> *Have sly puff on opium pipe?*

> *Hit plum brandy like no tomorrow?*

Night to remember turn out to be
nightmare wish to forget.

Host, life and soul of party
until midnight, when am overcome
with urgent need to meditate.
Bathroom full, so stagger into garden
in search of willow-tree.

Hours later, awake in ornamental pond
to sound of birdsong and heavy breathing.
Filled with dark foreboding
creep behind pagoda, where, to horror,
discover young wife, naked with lover!

No time to consider three thoughts.
One thrust of sword through back
of Lin Fang dispatch sinful couple
to shamed ancestors.

Heavy of heart, kneel at pond
to wash blood from hands. Startled
by ghostly reflection of unicorn.
Turn suddenly. Nothing but shadows
and faint thirrup of echoing hoofs.

Pondering significance, walk back
to house to send guests home.
Imagine horror at sight of Lin Fang
crosslegged on floor
idly divining oracle bones!

Calm self to think three times:

>*Seek advice from Confucius?*

>*Identify corpse?*

>*Set fire to pagoda and head for hills?*

Decide on first course of action –
    But Confucius nowhere to be found.

Resort to second course of action –
    Confucius in first stage of rigor mortis.

Settle on third course of action.

Hills very pleasant this time of year
Orchids in full bloom
Distant sighing of temple bell
But winter reigns in kingdom of heart.

Nightmares of unicorn
galloping across rickety bridge
young wife, naked, clinging to flowing mane.
In sky above, pair of bluebirds
in eternal embrace
skewered by single arrow.
Drops of blood
                    falling
                              into porcelain saucer
                                        of moon.

Also by Roger McGough